FLAGS

It was the Romans who probably used the first cloth banner. This was called a vexillum, and it is from this word that the name of the science of flags comes – vexillology (pronounced 'veks-ill-oll-oh-gee'). But the Roman vexillum was attached to as horizontal wooden spar in turn fixed to a vertical pole. A modern flag is usually attached to a rope so that it can be raised and lowered on a flagpole.

The first flags as we know them may have originated in the Far East. Every flag has its own unique story to tell about the history and hopes of the country whose national emblem it is. I-Spy Flags provides a fascinating way to learn about the ever-changing world we live in and some interesting facts about the countries.

The flags used within this I-Spy title are generally the national flag of the country indicated. A national flag is a flag that symbolises a country.

How to use your I-SPY book

The flags in this book are arranged in alphabetical order of the names of the counties whose emblems they are. Some flags are not easy to spot but, even if you Spy on television, you are entitled to half score. You need 1000 points to send off for your I-Spy certificate (see page 64) but that is not too difficult because there are masses of points in every book. As you make each l-Spy, write your score in the box.

I-SPY TITLES AVAILABLE:

- Ancient Britain
- Birds
- Cars
- Classic Cars
- Creepy Crawlies
- Flags
- Nature
- On a Car Journey
- On a Train Journey
- Trees
- Wild Flowers
- Working Vehicles

AFGHANISTAN

ALBANIA

Capital Kabul

Language Pashto, Dari (both official), Uzbek, Turkmen, Balochi, Pashai

Currency Afghani

Population 28,150,000

Area 652,225 sq km/ 251,825 sq mi

Political System in transition

Flag Black represents the occupation of foreigners, red represents the blood of freedom fighters, and green denotes Islam. In the middle of the flag is a mehrab, an arch in a mosque where the congregation stands, and a mender, a pulpit in a mosque. The mehrab and mender are both in white, and are enclosed by wheat.

I-SPY points: 15

Date: _____

Capital Tirana

Language Albanian (official), Greek

Currency Lek

Population 3,155,000

Area 28,748 sq km/11,099 sq mi

Political System Emergent democracy

Flag Red represents the bloodshed during the fight for independence. According to legend Albanians are descended from the eagle, which is the national emblem.

I-SPY points: 10

Date: _____

ALGERIA

Capital Algiers (Arabic al-Jaza'ir)

Language Arabic (official), Berber, French

Currency Algerian dinar

Population 34,895,000

Area 2,381,741 sq km/ 919,590 sq mi

Political System Military

Flag Red may suggest bloodshed or liberty. White symbolizes purity. Green represents Islam.

ANGOLA

Capital Luanda (and chief port)

Language Portuguese (official), Bantu, other native dialects

Currency Kwanza

Population 18,498,000

Area 1,246,700 sq km/ 481,350 sq mi

Political System Emergent democracy

Flag The yellow of the emblem is said to denote Angola's natural wealth. Red is said to stand for the blood spilt by the freedom fighters. Black represents Africa.

I-SPY points: 10

Date: _____

I-SPY points: 10

Date: _____

ARGENTINA

Capital Buenos Aires

Language Spanish (official) (95%), Italian (3%), English, German, French

Currency Peso (= 10,000 australs, which it replaced in 1992)

Population 40,276,000

Area 2,780,400 sq km/ 1,073,518 sq mi

Political System Liberal democracy

Flag The 'Sun of May' was added in 1818. The blue bands are a shade known as 'celeste', said to be the colour of the sky which inspired Argentine revolutionary Manuel Belgrano before battle.

AUSTRALIA

Capital Canberra

Language English (official), Aboriginal languages

Currency Australian dollar

Population 21,293,000

Area 7,682,850 sq km/ 2,966,136 sq mi

Political System Liberal democracy

Flag The Union Jack marks Australia's historical links with Britain. The Southern Cross helped guide early European navigators to the continent.

I-SPY points: 5

Date: _____

I-SPY points: 5

Date: _____

AUSTRIA

Capital Vienna

Language German (official)

Currency Euro (schilling until 2002)

Population 8,364,000

Area 83,859 sq km/32,367 sq mi

Political System Liberal democracy

Flag Red and white have been Austria's national colours for over 800 years.

AZERBAIJAN

Capital Baku

Language Azeri (official), Russian

Currency Manat (replaced Russian rouble in 1993)

Population 8,832,000

Area 86,600 sq km/33,436 sq mi

Political System Authoritarian nationalist

Flag The emblem recalls the flag of Turkey, a long-standing ally. The points of the star represent the eight Turkic tribes of Azerbaijan.

I-SPY points: 10

Date: _____

I-SPY points: 15

Date: _____

BAHAMAS

Capital Nassau (on New Providence island)

Language English (official), Creole

Currency Bahamian dollar

Population 342,000

Area 13,880 sq km/5,383 sq mi

Political System Liberal democracy

Flag Blue represents the Caribbean Sea. Yellow stands for the golden beaches.

BANGLADESH

formerly East Bengal (until 1955), East Pakistan (1955–71)

Capital Dhaka

Language Bengali (official), English

Currency Taka

Population 162,221,000 (2008 est)

Area 144,000 sq km/ 55,598 sq mi

Political System Emergent democracy

Flag The red disc, set towards the hoist, recalls the fight for independence. Green represents Islam, fertility, and the country's youth.

I-SPY points: 15

Date: _____

I-SPY points: 15

Date: _____

BARBADOS

Capital Bridgetown

Language English (official), Bajan (a Barbadian English dialect)

Currency Barbados dollar

Population 256,000

Area 430 sq km/166 sq mi

Political System Liberal democracy

Flag Blue represents the sea and the sky. The points of the trident represent the three principles of democracy: government of, for, and by the people.

BELGIUM

Capital Brussels

Language Flemish (spoken by 56%, mainly in Flanders, in the north), French (especially the dialect Walloon; official) (spoken by 32%, mainly in Wallonia, in the south), German (0.6%; mainly near the eastern border)

Currency Euro (Belgian franc until 2002)

Population 10,647,000

Area 30,510 sq km/11,779 sq mi

Political System Liberal democracy

Flag Modelled on the French tricolour, the vertical stripes represent liberty and revolution. The almost square proportions of the flag are unusual.

I-SPY points: 15

Date: _____

I-SPY points: 10

Date: _____

BOLIVIA

Capital La Paz (seat of government), Sucre (legal capital and seat of the judiciary)

Language Spanish (official) (4%), Aymara, Quechua

Currency Boliviano

Population 9,863,000

Area 1,098,581 sq km/ 424,162 sq mi

Political System Liberal democracy

Flag Red stands for Bolivia's animals and the valour of the liberating army. Green symbolizes fertility. Yellow represents Bolivia's mineral deposits.

BOSNIA-HERZEGOVINA

Capital Sarajevo

Language Serbian, Croat, Bosnian

Currency Konvertable mark

Population 3,767,000

Area 51,129 sq km/19,740 sq mi

Political System Emergent democracy

Flag The stars on a blue field represent Europe. The yellow triangle stands for equality between the three peoples of Bosnia-Herzegovina.

I-SPY points: 15

Date: _____

I-SPY points: 15

Date: _____

BRAZIL

Capital Brasilia

Language Portuguese (official), Spanish, English, French, 120 Indian languages

Currency Real

Population 193,734,000

Area 8,511,965 sq km/ 3,286,469 sq mi

Political System Liberal democracy

Flag Yellow and the diamond shape represent Brazil's mineral wealth. The motto 'Ordem e Progresso' means 'Order and Progress'. Green stands for the vast forests.

BULGARIA

Capital Sofia

Language Bulgarian (official), Turkish

Currency Lev

Population 7,545,000

Area 110,912 sq km/ 42,823 sq mi

Political System Emergent democracy

Flag White represents a desire for peace and liberty. Green symbolizes freedom and agricultural wealth. Red stands for the courage of spilt blood of the freedom fighters.

I-SPY points: 5

Date: _____

10

I-SPY points: 10

Date: _____

CAMBODIA

formerly Khmer Republic (1970–76), Kampuchea (1976–89)

Capital Phnom Penh

Language Khmer (official), French

Currency Cambodian riel

Population 14,805,000

Area 181,035 sq km/ 69,897 sq mi

Political System Emergent democracy

Flag The temple of Angkor Wat had five towers but often only three are depicted. Red and blue recall the earlier flags of Cambodia.

CAMEROON

formerly Kamerun (until 1916)

Capital Yaoundé

Language French, English (both official; often spoken in pidgin), Sudanic languages (in the north), Bantu languages (elsewhere); there has been some discontent with the emphasis on French - there are 163 indigenous peoples with their own African languages

Currency Franc CFA

Population 19,522,000

Area 475,440 sq km/ 183,567 sq mi

Political System Emergent democracy

Flag The single star represents the unity of the former French and British territories.

I-SPY points: 15

Date: _____

I-SPY points: 15

Date: _____

CANADA

Capital Ottawa

Language English (60%), French (24%) (both official), American Indian languages, Inuktitut (Inuit)

Currency Canadian dollar

Population 33,573,000

Area 9,970,610 sq km/ 3,849,652 sq mi

Political System Liberal democracy

Flag The maple leaf is a traditional Canadian emblem. Red recalls Canadian lives lost during World War I. White stands for snow.

CENTRAL AFRICAN REPUBLIC

formerly Central African Empire (1976–79)

Capital Bangui

Language French (official), Sangho (national), Arabic, Hunsa, Swahili

Currency Franc CFA

Population 4,422,000

Area 622,436 sq km/ 240,322 sq mi

Political System Emergent democracy

Flag Red, white, and blue recall the French tricolour. Red, yellow, and green are the pan-African colours. Red represents the common blood of mankind which links African and European nations.

I-SPY points: 5

I-SPY points: 15

Date: _____

CHAD

Capital Ndjamena (formerly Fort Lamy)

Language French, Arabic (both official), over 100 African languages

Currency Franc CFA

Population 11,206,000

Area 1,284,000 sq km/ 495,752 sq mi

Political System Emergent democracy

Flag Blue symbolizes hope, the clear sky, and the streams of the south. Yellow stands for the sun and the Sahara Desert. Red represents unity, prosperity, and national sacrifice.

CHILE

Capital Santiago

Language Spanish (official)

Currency Chilean peso

Population 16,970,000

Area 756,950 sq km/ 292,258 sq mi

Political System Emergent democracy

Flag White stands for the snowy peaks of the Andes. Red symbolizes the blood shed by the freedom fighters. Blue represents the clear Andean skies.

I-SPY points: 15

Date:

I-SPY points: 10

Date:

CHINA

Capital Beijing (or Peking)

Language Chinese (dialects include Mandarin (official), Yue (Cantonese), Wu (Shanghaiese), Minbai, Minnah, Xiang, Gan, and Hakka)

Currency Yuan

Population 1,345,751,000

Area 9,572,900 sq km/ 3,696,000 sq mi

Political System Communist

Flag The large star symbolizes the common programme of the Communist Party. The small stars represent the four economic classes: peasants, workers, petty bourgeoisie, and 'patriotic capitalists'. The star represents a guide to progress and honour.

COLOMBIA

Capital Bogotá

Language Spanish (official) (95%)

Currency Colombian peso

Population 45,660,000

Area 1,141,748 sq km/ 440,828 sq mi

Political System Liberal democracy

Flag Yellow represents the golden land of South America. Blue stands for the ocean separating the country from Spain. Red symbolizes the blood and courage of the people resisting the tyrants.

I-SPY points: 5

Date: _____

I-SPY points: 15

Date: _____

COSTA RICA

Capital San Jose

Language Spanish (official)

Currency Colon

Population 4,579,000

Area 51,100 sq km/
19,729 sq mi

Political System Liberal
democracy

Flag Blue for the sky and
opportunities, white for wisdom,
happiness and clear-thinking.
Red was added to the blue and
white flag to reflect the French
tricolour.

CÔTE D'IVOIRE

Capital Yamoussoukro

Language French (official), over
60 ethnic languages

Currency Franc CFA

Population 21,075,000

Area 322,463 sq km/
124,502 sq mi

Political System Emergent
democracy

Flag Orange stands for the
savannah. White symbolizes the
country's rivers. Green represents
the forests.

I-SPY points: 15

Date: _____

I-SPY points: 10

Date: _____

CROATIA

Capital Zagreb
Language Croat (official), Serbian
Currency Kuna
Population 4,416,000
Area 56,538 sq km/21,829 sq mi
Political System Emergent democracy
Flag Red, white, and blue are the pan-Slav colours. The small shields represent Croatia Ancient, Dubrovnik, Dalmatia, Istria, and Slavonia. The flag is based on the tricolour used during World War II.

CUBA

Capital Havana
Language Spanish (official)
Currency Cuban peso
Population 11,204,000
Area 110,860 sq km/ 42,803 sq mi
Political System Communist
Flag The flag is known as the 'Lone Star' banner. The red triangle symbolizes the blood shed in the fight for freedom from Spain. The blue stripes stand for Cuba's three provinces.

I-SPY points: 10

Date: _____

I-SPY points: 15

Date: _____

CZECH REPUBLIC

formerly Czechoslovakia (with Slovakia) (1918–93)

Capital Prague

Language Czech (official), Slovak

Currency Koruna (based on the Czechoslovak koruna)

Population 10,369,000

Area 78,864 sq km/30,449 sq mi

Political System Liberal democracy

Flag Red and white are the colours of Bohemia, dating back to the 13th century. Blue represents Moravia. Unlike that of the Slovak Republic, the Czech flag is not based on the pan-Slav colours.

DENMARK

Capital Copenhagen

Language Danish (official)

Currency Danish krone

Population 5,470,000

Area 43,075 sq km/16,631 sq mi

Political System Liberal democracy

Flag Nordic flags bearing the Scandinavian cross are based on the Danish flag, known as the Dannebrog, 'Danish cloth'.

I-SPY points: 5

Date: _____

I-SPY points: 5

Date: _____

DOMINICAN REPUBLIC

formerly Hispaniola (with Haiti) (until 1844)

Capital Santo Domingo

Language Spanish (official)

Currency Dominican Republic peso

Population 10,090,000

Area 48,442 sq km/18,703 sq mi

Political System Liberal democracy

Flag The arms show a Bible open at the Gospel of St John, a Trinitarian symbol. The white cross symbolizes faith. The arms appear on national and state flags.

ECUADOR

Capital Quito

Language Spanish (official), Quechua, Jivaro, other indigenous languages

Currency US dollar

Population 13,625,000

Area 270,670 sq km/ 104,505 sq mi

Political System Liberal democracy

Flag A condor, poised to attack enemies, protects the nation under its wings. Blue symbolizes independence from Spain. Yellow recalls the Federation of Greater Colombia. Red stands for courage.

I-SPY points: 15

Date: _____

I-SPY points: 15

Date: _____

EGYPT

Capital Cairo

Language Arabic (official), Coptic (derived from ancient Egyptian), English, French

Currency Egyptian pound

Population 82,999,000

Area 1,001,450 sq km/ 386,659 sq mi

Political System Liberal democracy

Flag Red, white, and black are the colours of Arab nationalism.

EL SALVADOR

Capital San Salvador

Language Spanish (official), Nahuatl

Currency US dollar (replaced Salvadorean colon in 2001)

Population 6,163,000

Area 21,393 sq km/8,259 sq mi

Political System Emergent democracy

Flag The blue-white-blue flag remembers the Central American federation from the middle of the 19th century. The arms may be replaced by the motto Dios, Union, Libertad, 'God, Union, Liberty'.

I-SPY points: 10

Date: _____

I-SPY points: 10

Date: _____

ESTONIA

Capital Tallinn

Language Estonian (official), Russian

Currency Kroon

Population 1,340,000

Area 45,000 sq km/17,374 sq mi

Political System Emergent democracy

Flag Blue stands for faith and loyalty, the sea, lakes, and the sky. Black represents past suffering and is the colour of the traditional peasant's jacket. White symbolizes virtue and enlightenment and is the colour of snow, birch bark, and the midnight sun.

ETHIOPIA

formerly Abyssinia (until the 1920s)

Capital Addis Ababa

Language Amharic (official), Arabic, Tigrinya, Orominga, about 100 other local languages

Currency Ethiopian birr

Population 82,825,000

Area 1,096,900 sq km/ 423,513 sq mi

Political System Emergent democracy

Flag Blue stands for peace. Red represents power and faith. Yellow stands for the church, peace, natural wealth, and love. Green symbolizes the land and hope.

I-SPY points: 10

Date: _____

I-SPY points: 10

Date: _____

FINLAND

Capital Helsinki (Swedish Helsingfors)

Language Finnish (93%), Swedish (6%) (both official), Saami (Lapp), Russian

Currency Euro (markka until 2002)

Population 5,326,000

Area 338,145 sq km/ 130,557 sq mi

Political System Liberal democracy

Flag Blue represents Finland's 60,000 lakes. White stands for the snow which covers the ground for 5–7 months each year.

FRANCE

Capital Paris

Language French (official; regional languages include Basque, Breton, Catalan, Corsican, and Provencal)

Currency Euro (franc until 2002)

Population 62,343,000 (including Corsica)

Area 543,965 sq km/ 210,024 sq mi

Political System Liberal democracy

Flag Red and blue were taken from the arms of Paris. White was the colour of the Bourbon dynasty.

I-SPY points: 5

Date: _____

I-SPY points: 5

Date: _____

GAMBIA, THE

Capital Banjul

Language English (official), Mandinka, Fula, Wolof, other indigenous dialects

Currency Dalasi

Population 1,705,000

Area 10,402 sq km/4,016 sq mi

Political System Transitional

Flag Red represents the sun. Blue stands for the Gambia river. Green symbolizes agriculture.

GEORGIA

Capital Tbilisi

Language Georgian (official), Russian, Abkazian, Armenian, Azeri

Currency Lari

Population 4,260,000

Area 69,700 sq km/26,911 sq mi

Political System Emergent democracy

Flag Adapted from a 14th-century flag, the red St. George's cross in the centre represents the country's patron saint. The layout - the larger cross connecting the four sides of the flag with a smaller cross in each of the corners - is based on the historical Jerusalem Cross.

I-SPY points: 15

Date: _____

I-SPY points: 15

Date: _____

GERMANY

Capital Berlin

Language German (official)

Currency Euro (Deutschmark until 2002)

Population 82,167,000

Area 357,041 sq km/ 137,853 sq mi

Political System Liberal democracy

Flag Black and red recall the tunics worn by soldiers during the Napoleonic wars. Gold was added to create a flag similar to the French tricolour, a symbol of revolution.

GHANA
formerly the Gold Coast (until 1957)

Capital Accra

Language English (official), Ga, other African languages

Currency Cedi

Population 23,837,000

Area 238,540 sq km/ 92,100 sq mi

Political System Emergent democracy

Flag Ghana was the first country to adopt the pan-African colours. The star is known as the 'lode star of African freedom'.

I-SPY points: 5

Date: _____

I-SPY points: 10

Date: _____

GREECE

Capital Athens

Language Greek (official)

Currency Euro (drachma until 2002)

Population 11,161,000

Area 131,957 sq km/ 50,948 sq mi

Political System Liberal democracy

Flag The cross represents the Greek Orthodox faith. Blue stands for the sea and sky. The shade has varied over the years. White symbolizes purity.

GRENADA

Capital St George's

Language English (official), some French-African patois

Currency East Caribbean dollar

Population 104,000 (including the southern Grenadine Islands, notably Carriacou and Petit Martinique)

Area 344 sq km/133 sq mi

Political System Liberal democracy

Flag Yellow represents sunshine, warmth, and wisdom. Green symbolizes the lush vegetation and agriculture.

I-SPY points: 5

Date: _____

I-SPY points: 15

Date: _____

GUATEMALA

Capital Guatemala City

Language Spanish (official), 22 Mayan languages (45%)

Currency Quetzal

Population 14,027,000

Area 108,889 sq km/ 42,042 sq mi

Political System Liberal democracy

Flag The quetzal, the national bird of Guatemala, symbolizes freedom. The blue bands stand for the Caribbean Sea and the Pacific Ocean. The weapons represent the defence of liberty.

HAITI

formerly Hispaniola (with Dominican Republic) (until 1844)

Capital Port-au-Prince

Language French (20%), Creole (both official)

Currency Gourde

Population 10,033,000

Area 27,750 sq km/10,714 sq mi

Political System Transitional

Flag Blue represents the black population and links with Africa. Red stands for those of mixed race. The original blue and red flag was based on the French tricolour.

I-SPY points: 20

Date: _____

I-SPY points: 15

Date: _____

HONDURAS

Capital Tegucigalpa

Language Spanish (official), English, American Indian languages

Currency Lempira

Population 7,466,000

Area 112,100 sq km/ 43,281 sq mi

Political System Liberal democracy

Flag The blue and white triband is based on the flag of the Central American Federation (CAF), a grouping of African states imposed by the British government in 1953. The stars represent the Federation's five original members.

HUNGARY

Capital Budapest

Language Hungarian (official)

Currency Forint

Population 9,993,000

Area 93,032 sq km/35,919 sq mi

Political System Liberal democracy

Flag Red stands for strength. White symbolizes faithfulness. Green represents hope.

I-SPY points: 20

Date: _____

I-SPY points: 10

Date: _____

26

ICELAND

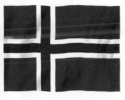

Capital Reykjavik

Language Icelandic (official)

Currency Krona

Population 323,000

Area 103,000 sq km/ 39,768 sq mi

Political System Liberal democracy

Flag Red symbolizes the fire from Iceland's volcanos. White represents ice. Blue stands for the mountains.

INDIA

Capital New Delhi

Language Hindi, English, Assamese, Bengali, Gujarati, Kannada, Kashmiri, Konkani, Malayalam, Manipuri, Marathi, Nepali, Oriya, Punjabi, Sanskrit, Sindhi, Tamil, Telugu, Urdu

Currency Rupee

Population 1,198,003,000

Area 3,166,829 sq km/ 1,222,713 sq mi

Political System Liberal democracy

Flag Orange represents courage and sacrifice. White represents truth, purity, and peace. Green represents faith, fertility, and chivalry. The emblem is the Ashoka Chakra ('Wheel of the Law').

I-SPY points: 10

Date: _____

I-SPY points: 10

Date: _____

INDONESIA
formerly Dutch East Indies (until 1949)

Capital Jakarta

Language Bahasa Indonesia (closely related to Malay; official), Javanese, Dutch, over 550 regional languages and dialects

Currency Rupiah

Population 229,965,000

Area 1,904,569 sq km/ 735,354 sq mi

Political System Emergent democracy

Flag Red represents the body as well as gallantry and freedom. White stands for the soul, purity, and justice.

IRAN
formerly Persia (until 1935)

Capital Tehran

Language Persian (Farsi (official), Kurdish, Turkish, Arabic, English, French

Currency Rial

Population 74,196,000

Area 1,648,000 sq km/ 636,292 sq mi

Political System Islamic nationalist

Flag Green represents Islam. White symbolizes peace. Red stands for courage.

I-SPY points: 15

Date: _____

I-SPY points: 10

Date: _____

IRAQ

Capital Baghdad

Language Arabic (80%) (official), Kurdish (15%), Assyrian, Armenian

Currency Iraqi dinar

Population 30,747,000

Area 434,924 sq km/ 167,924 sq mi

Political System Evolving

Flag Red stands for courage. White represents generosity. Black symbolizes Islamic triumphs. The green on the white band is Arabic script meaning 'God is great'.

IRELAND, REPUBLIC OF
or Éire

Capital Dublin

Language Irish Gaelic, English (both official)

Currency Euro (Irish pound, or punt Eireannach, until 2002)

Population 4,515,000

Area 70,282 sq km/ 27,135 sq mi

Political System Liberal democracy

Flag Green represents the Catholic people. Orange stands for the Protestant people. White is a symbol of peace.

I-SPY points: 10

Date: _____

I-SPY points: 10

Date: _____

ISRAEL

Capital Jerusalem (not recognized by the United Nations)

Language Hebrew, Arabic (both official), English, Yiddish, other European and west Asian languages

Currency Shekel

Population 7,170,000

Area 20,800 sq km/8,030 sq mi (as at 1949 armistice)

Political System Liberal democracy

Flag The Star of David is a centuries-old symbol of Judaism. Blue and white are traditional Jewish colours.

ITALY

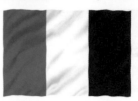

Capital Rome

Language Italian (official), German and Ladin (in the north), French (in the Valle d'Aosta region), Greek and Albanian (in the south)

Currency Euro (lira until 2002)

Population 59,870,000

Area 301,300 sq km/ 116,331 sq mi

Political System Liberal democracy

Flag The colours of the flag date from Napoleon's invasion in 1796. The design is based on the French tricolour.

I-SPY points: 10

Date: _____

I-SPY points: 5

Date: _____

JAMAICA

Capital Kingston

Language English (official), Jamaican Creole

Currency Jamaican dollar

Population 2,719,000

Area 10,957 sq km/4,230 sq mi

Political System Liberal democracy

Flag Black, yellow, and green are colours found in many African flags and reflect the islanders' heritage.

JAPAN

Capital Tokyo

Language Japanese (official), Ainu

Currency Yen

Population 127,156,000

Area 377,535 sq km/ 145,766 sq mi

Political System Liberal democracy

Flag The mon, the central red disc, is called Hi-no-maru or sun-disc. The disc is set slightly towards the hoist. White symbolizes honesty and purity.

I-SPY points: 10

Date: _____

I-SPY points: 5

Date: _____

JORDAN

Capital Amman

Language Arabic (official), English

Currency Jordanian dinar

Population 6,316,000

Area 89,206 sq km/34,442 sq mi (excluding the West Bank 5,879 sq km/2,269 sq mi)

Political System Emergent democracy

Flag The points of the star represent the first seven verses of the Koran. Red, black, white, and green became the pan-Arab colours.

KAZAKHSTAN

Capital Astana (formerly Akmola)

Language Kazakh (related to Turkish; official), Russian

Currency Tenge

Population 15,637,000

Area 2,717,300 sq km/ 1,049,150 sq mi

Political System Authoritarian nationalist

Flag Blue represents the sky. The golden sun symbolizes the country's hopes for the future.

I-SPY points: 15

Date: _____

I-SPY points: 20

Date: _____

KENYA

Capital Nairobi

Language English, Kiswahili (both official), many local dialects

Currency Kenyan shilling

Population 39,802,000

Area 582,600 sq km/ 224,941 sq mi

Political System Authoritarian nationalist

Flag Black stands for the African people. White symbolizes peace. Black, red, and green, the 'black liberation' colours, denote Africa's rebirth. Red represents the blood common to all people. Green recalls the fertile land.

KOREA, NORTH

Capital Pyongyang

Language Korean (official)

Currency Won

Population 23,906,000

Area 120,538 sq km/ 46,539 sq mi

Political System Communist

Flag White stands for purity. Red represents communist revolution. Blue expresses the desire for peace.

I-SPY points: 10

Date: _____

I-SPY points: 10

Date: _____

KOREA, SOUTH

Capital Seoul

Language Korean (official)

Currency Won

Population 48,333,000

Area 98,799 sq km/38,146 sq mi

Political System Liberal democracy

Flag The top left trigram symbolizes summer, south, and heaven. The top right trigram represents autumn, west, and the moon. The bottom right trigram stands for winter, north, and the Earth. The bottom left trigram represents spring, east, and the sun.

KUWAIT

Capital Kuwait (and chief port)

Language Arabic (78%) (official), English, Kurdish (10%), Farsi (4%)

Currency Kuwaiti dinar

Population 2,985,000

Area 17,819 sq km/6,879 sq mi

Political System Absolutist

Flag The flag uses the pan-Arab colours. The design may have been inspired by the pre-1958 Iraqi flag.

I-SPY points: 5

Date: _____

I-SPY points: 10

Date: _____

LATVIA

LEBANON

Capital Riga

Language Latvian (official)

Currency Lat

Population 2,249,000

Area 63,700 sq km/24,594 sq mi

Political System Emergent democracy

Flag It is said that berries were used to dye the flag. Red represents the blood shed in the past and the willingness to offer it again. White stands for right, truth, the honour of free citizens, and trustworthiness.

Capital Beirut (and chief port)

Language Arabic (official), French, Armenian, English

Currency Lebanese pound

Population 4,224,000

Area 10,452 sq km/4,035 sq mi

Political System Emergent democracy

Flag Red is said to stand for bloodshed. White represents peace, holiness, and eternity. The cedar tree is the symbol of the country as Lebanon has many cedar forests.

I-SPY points: 15

Date: _____

I-SPY points: 15

Date: _____

LIBERIA

Capital Monrovia (and chief port)

Language English (official), over 20 Niger-Congo languages

Currency Liberian dollar

Population 3,955,000

Area 111,370 sq km/ 42,999 sq mi

Political System Emergent democracy

Flag The star depicts Liberia as a shining light. The blue canton symbolizes the dark continent of Africa. The stripes represent the 11 signatories to the Declaration of Independence.

LIBYA

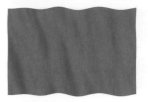

Capital Tripoli

Language Arabic (official), Italian, English

Currency Libyan dinar

Population 6,420,000

Area 1,759,540 sq km/ 679,358 sq mi

Political System Nationalistic socialist

Flag The flag was said to represent the nation's hope for a green revolution in agriculture. Green expresses the people's Muslim faith.

I-SPY points: 15

Date:

I-SPY points: 15

Date:

LIECHTENSTEIN

Capital Vaduz

Language German (official), an Alemannic dialect

Currency Swiss franc

Population 36,000

Area 160 sq km/62 sq mi

Political System Liberal democracy

Flag The crown emblem was modernized in 1982. The colours date back to the 18th century.

LITHUANIA

Capital Vilnius

Language Lithuanian (official)

Currency Litas

Population 3,287,000

Area 65,200 sq km/25,173 sq mi

Political System Emergent democracy

Flag Yellow stands for grain and freedom from need. Green symbolizes the forests and hope. Red represents bloodshed and courage.

I-SPY points: 20
Date: _____

I-SPY points: 15
Date: _____

LUXEMBOURG

Capital Luxembourg

Language Letzeburgisch (a German-Moselle-Frankish dialect; official), English

Currency Euro (Luxembourg franc until 2002)

Population 486,000

Area 2,586 sq km/998 sq mi

Political System Liberal democracy

Flag The blue band is lighter than that of the Dutch tricolour.

MACEDONIA

Capital Skopje

Language Macedonian (related to Bulgarian; official), Albanian

Currency Macedonian denar

Population 2,042,000

Area 25,700 sq km/9,922 sq mi

Political System Emergent democracy

Flag Red and yellow were the colours of Macedonia's flag when the republic was part of Yugoslavia

I-SPY points: 10

Date: _____

I-SPY points: 20

Date: _____

MADAGASCAR

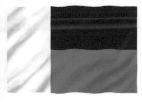

Capital Antananarivo

Language Malagasy, French (both official), local dialects

Currency Malagasy franc

Population 19,625,000

Area 587,041 sq km/ 226,656 sq mi

Political System Emergent democracy

Flag Red stands for sovereignty. White represents purity. Green recalls the coastal inhabitants and is a symbol of hope.

MALAYSIA

Capital Kuala Lumpur

Language Bahasa Malaysia (Malay; official), English, Chinese, Tamil, Iban, many local dialects

Currency Ringgit

Population 27,468,000

Area 329,759 sq km/ 127,319 sq mi

Political System Liberal democracy

Flag Red and white are the traditional colours of South East Asia. The blue canton recalls the British Empire and represents unity. Yellow is the colour of the Sultans of Malaysia.

I-SPY points: 15

Date: _____

I-SPY points: 15

Date: _____

MALDIVES

Capital Male

Language Divehi (a Sinhalese dialect; official), English, Arabic

Currency Rufiya

Population 309,000

Area 298 sq km/115 sq mi

Political System Authoritarian nationalist

Flag The green panel and the crescent represent Islam. Red recalls the original flag.

MALI

Capital Bamako

Language French (official), Bambara, other African languages

Currency Franc CFA

Population 13,010,000

Area 1,240,142 sq km/ 478,818 sq mi

Political System Emergent democracy

Flag Green, yellow, and red are the pan-African colours. The flag is modelled on the French tricolour. The design was identical to the Rwandan tricolour, obliging that country to modify its flag.

I-SPY points: 20

Date: _____

I-SPY points: 15

Date: _____

MALTA

Capital Valletta (and chief port)

Language Maltese, English (both official)

Currency Maltese lira

Population 409,000

Area 320 sq km/124 sq mi

Political System Liberal democracy

Flag The George Cross was awarded by King George VI and originally appeared in a small blue canton. The present design dates from 1964 when the islands gained independence.

MAURITIUS

Capital Port Louis (and chief port)

Language English (official), French, Creole (36%), Bhojpuri (32%), other Indian languages

Currency Mauritian rupee

Population 1,288,000

Area 1,865 sq km/720 sq mi

Political System Liberal democracy

Flag Red recalls the struggle for independence. Blue stands for the Indian Ocean. Yellow expresses hope for a bright future. Green represents agriculture and vegetation.

I-SPY points: 10

Date: _____

I-SPY points: 15

Date: _____

MEXICO

Capital Mexico City

Language Spanish (official), Nahuatl, Maya, Zapoteco, Mixteco, Otomi

Currency Mexican peso

Population 109,610,000

Area 1,958,201 sq km/ 756,061 sq mi

Political System Liberal democracy

Flag The emblem was added to distinguish the flag from that of Italy. The design is based on the French tricolour. The colours are those of the Mexican liberation army.

MONACO

Capital Monaco

Language French (official), Monegasgne (a mixture of the French Provencal and Italian Ligurian dialects), Italian

Currency Euro

Population 33,000

Area 1.95 sq km/0.75 sq mi

Political System Liberal democracy

Flag The flag's colours date back to the 14th century. The bicolour is identical to that of Indonesia except in its ratio

I-SPY points: 10

Date: _____

I-SPY points: 15

Date: _____

MONGOLIA

Capital Ulaanbaatar

Language Khalkha Mongolian (official), Kazakh (in the province of Bagan-Olgiy), Chinese, Russian, Turkic languages

Currency Tugrik

Population 2,671,000

Area 1,565,000 sq km/ 604,246 sq mi

Political System Emergent democracy

Flag Red represents progress. Blue is Mongolia's national colour.

MOROCCO

Capital Rabat

Language Arabic (75%) (official), Berber dialects (25%), French, Spanish

Currency Dirham

Population 31,993,000

Area 458,730 sq km/177,115 sq mi (excluding Western Sahara)

Political System Emergent democracy

Flag The 'Solomon's Seal' pentagram was added to distinguish the flag from other plain red Arab banners.

I-SPY points: 15

Date: _____

I-SPY points: 15

Date: _____

MOZAMBIQUE

Capital Maputo (and chief port)

Language Portuguese (official), 16 African languages

Currency Metical

Population 22,894,000

Area 799,380 sq km/ 308,640 sq mi

Political System Emergent democracy

Flag Green stands for agriculture. Red recalls the struggle for independence. White denotes peace. Yellow symbolizes mineral wealth.

NAMIBIA

Capital Windhoek

Language English (official), Afrikaans, German, Ovambo (51%), Nama (12%), Kavango (10%), other indigenous languages

Currency Namibian dollar

Population 2,171,000

Area 824,300 sq km/ 318,262 sq mi

Political System Emergent democracy

Flag Blue recalls the clear sky, the Atlantic Ocean, water, and rain. Red represents Namibia's people reflecting their heroism and desire for equal opportunity. White stands for peace and unity. Green symbolizes vegetation and agriculture.

I-SPY points: 15

Date: _____

I-SPY points: 20

Date: _____

NEPAL

Capital Kathmandu

Language Nepali (official), Tibetan, numerous local languages

Currency Nepalese rupee

Population 29,331,000

Area 147,181 sq km/ 56,826 sq mi

Political System Emergent democracy

Flag Initially the sun and moon had human faces, but they were removed when the flag was updated in 1962. The flag is said to express the hope that Nepal will endure as long as the sun and the moon. The blue border symbolizes peace.

NETHERLANDS, THE

Capital Amsterdam (official), the Hague (legislative and judicial)

Language Dutch (official)

Currency Euro (guilder until 2002)

Population 16,592,000

Area 41,863 sq km/16,163 sq mi

Political System Liberal democracy

Flag The number of stripes changed frequently until around 1800. Red, white, and blue became the colours of liberty and an inspiration for other revolutionary flags around the world.

I-SPY points: 25

Date: _____

I-SPY points: 5

Date: _____

NEW ZEALAND

Capital Wellington

Language English (official), Maori

Currency New Zealand dollar

Population 4,266,000

Area 268,680 sq km/ 103,737 sq mi

Political System Liberal democracy

Flag The Union Jack marks New Zealand's historical links with Britain. The stars represent the Southern Cross.

NIGERIA

Capital Abuja

Language English (official), Hausa, Ibo, Yoruba

Currency Naira

Population 154,729,000

Area 923,773 sq km/ 356,668 sq mi

Political System Emergent democracy

Flag Green stands for Nigeria's forests and agriculture. White represents the River Niger, peace, and unity.

I-SPY points: 5

Date: _____

I-SPY points: 15

Date: _____

NORWAY

Capital Oslo

Language Norwegian (official), Saami (Lapp), Finnish

Currency Norwegian krone

Population 4,812,000

Area 387,000 sq km/ 149,420 sq mi (including Svalbard and Jan Mayen)

Political System Liberal democracy

Flag Blue is taken from the Swedish arms. Red and white recall the Danish flag, known as the Dannebrog.

PAKISTAN

Capital Islamabad

Language Urdu (official), English, Punjabi, Sindhi, Pashto, Baluchi, other local dialects

Currency Pakistan rupee

Population 180,808,000

Area 803,940 sq km/ 310,321 sq mi

Political System Military

Flag Green represents Islam. The combination of green and white symbolizes peace and prosperity.

I-SPY points: 5
Date: _____

I-SPY points: 10
Date: _____

47

PARAGUAY

Capital Asunción (and chief river port)

Language Spanish (official), Guarani (an indigenous Indian language)

Currency Guarani

Population 6,349,000

Area 406,752 sq km/ 157,046 sq mi

Political System Emergent democracy

Flag The Star of May recalls the declaration of independence on 14 May 1811. The colours were inspired by the French tricolour.

PERU

Capital Lima

Language Spanish, Quechua (both official), Aymara, many indigenous dialects

Currency Nuevo sol

Population 29,165,000

Area 1,285,200 sq km/ 496,216 sq mi

Political System Liberal democracy

Flag Red and white were the colours of the Inca Empire. Red represents the blood shed in the fight for independence. White stands for peace and justice.

I-SPY points: 10

Date: _____

I-SPY points: 15

Date: _____

PHILIPPINES

Capital Manila (on Luzon island) (and chief port)

Language Filipino, English (both official), Spanish, Cebuano, Ilocano, more than 70 other indigenous languages

Currency Peso

Population 91,983,000

Area 300,000 sq km/ 115,830 sq mi

Political System Liberal democracy

Flag Blue expresses patriotism and noble ideas. Red denotes bravery. White symbolizes peace and purity. The stars stand for the three island groups: Luzon, the Visayan, and Mindanao.

POLAND

Capital Warsaw

Language Polish (official)

Currency Zloty

Population 38,074,000

Area 312,683 sq km/ 120,726 sq mi

Political System Liberal democracy

Flag Red and white are the national colours, derived from a 13th-century emblem bearing a white eagle on a red field.

I-SPY points: 15

Date: _____

I-SPY points: 5

Date: _____

PORTUGAL

Capital Lisbon

Language Portuguese (official)

Currency Euro (escudo until 2002)

Population 10,707,000

Area 92,000 sq km/35,521 sq mi (including the Azores and Madeira)

Political System Liberal democracy

Flag Green and red replaced blue and white as the national colours in 1910. The armillary sphere surrounds the shield of Portugal.

ROMANIA

Capital Bucharest

Language Romanian (official), Hungarian, German

Currency Leu

Population 21,275,000

Area 237,500 sq km/ 91,698 sq mi

Political System Liberal democracy

Flag Nowadays the colours are said to stand for Moldavia, Transylvania, and Wallachia.

I-SPY points: 5

Date: _____

I-SPY points: 10

Date: _____

RUSSIAN FEDERATION OR RUSSIA

formerly Russian Soviet Federal Socialist Republic (until 1991)

Capital Moscow

Language Russian (official) and many East Slavic, Altaic, Uralic, Caucasian languages

Currency Rouble

Population 140,874,000

Area 17,075,400 sq km/ 6,592,811 sq mi

Political System Emergent democracy

Flag White, blue, and red became known as the pan-Slavic colours, influencing many other Eastern European flags. White, blue, and red are also the colours of the arms of the Duchy of Moscow.

I-SPY points: 15

Date: _____

SAUDI ARABIA

Capital Riyadh

Language Arabic (official), English

Currency Riyal

Population 25,721,000

Area 2,200,518 sq km/ 849,620 sq mi

Political System Absolutist Abdulla from 2005

Flag The prophet Muhammad is said to have used a green banner. Past variants of the flag show two crossed swords.

I-SPY points: 20

Date: _____

SINGAPORE

formerly part of Straits Settlement (1826–1942), part of the Federation of Malaysia (1963–65)

Capital Singapore City

Language Malay, Mandarin Chinese, Tamil, English (all official), other Indian languages, Chinese dialects

Currency Singapore dollar

Population 4,737,000

Area 622 sq km/240 sq mi

Political System Liberal democracy

Flag Red and white are traditional colours in South East Asia. Red represents universal fellowship and equality. White stands for purity and virtue.

SLOVAK REPUBLIC

formerly Czechoslovakia (with the Czech Republic) (1918–93)

Capital Bratislava

Language Slovak (official), Hungarian, Czech, other ethnic languages

Currency Slovak koruna (based on Czechoslovak koruna)

Population 5,406,000

Area 49,035 sq km/18,932 sq mi

Political System Emergent democracy

Flag The arms depict the Carpathian Mountains which traverse the Slovak Republic. The flag uses the pan-Slav colours representing liberation from foreign domination.

I-SPY points: 10

Date:

I-SPY points: 10

Date:

SLOVENIA

Capital Ljubljana

Language Slovene (related to Serbo-Croat; official), Hungarian, Italian

Currency Tolar

Population 2,020,000

Area 20,251 sq km/7,818 sq mi

Political System Emergent democracy

Flag The three stars are taken from the arms of the Duchy of Selje. The flag uses the pan-Slav colours.

SOUTH AFRICA

Capital Cape Town (legislative), Pretoria (administrative), Bloemfontein (judicial), Johannesburg (commercial)

Language English, Afrikaans, Xhosa, Zulu, Sesotho (all official), other African languages

Currency Rand

Population 50,110,000

Area 1,222,081 sq km/ 471,845 sq mi

Political System Emergent democracy

Flag Black, green, and yellow are the African National Congress (ANC) colours. Red, white, and blue are the colours of the former Dutch republics.

I-SPY points: 10
Date: _____

I-SPY points: 5
Date: _____

SPAIN

Capital Madrid

Language Spanish (Castilian; official), Basque, Catalan, Galician

Currency Euro (peseta until 2002)

Population 44,904,000

Area 504,750 sq km/194,883 sq mi (including the Balearic and Canary islands)

Political System Liberal democracy

Flag The Pillars of Hercules represent the promontories of Gibraltar and Ceuta. The shield represents the regions of Castile, Léon, Aragón, Navarre, and Granada.

SRI LANKA
formerly Ceylon (until 1972)

Capital Sri Jayewardenapura Kottead (administrative), Colombo (commercial)

Language Sinhala, Tamil (both official), English

Currency Sri Lankan rupee

Population 20,238,000

Area 65,610 sq km/25,332 sq mi

Political System Liberal democracy

Flag Green represents the Islamic minority. Orange stands for the Hindu Tamils. The sword denotes authority. The four pipul leaves symbolize Buddhism

I-SPY points: 5

Date: _____

I-SPY points: 20

Date: _____

SWEDEN

Capital Stockholm

Language Swedish (official), Finnish, Saami (Lapp)

Currency Swedish krona

Population 9,249,000

Area 450,000 sq km/ 173,745 sq mi

Political System Liberal democracy

Flag The colours are derived from the state coat of arms of 1364. The Scandinavian cross is taken from the Danish flag.

SWITZERLAND

Capital Bern

Language German (65%), French (18%), Italian (10%), Romansch (1%) (all official)

Currency Swiss franc

Population 7,568,000

Area 41,300 sq km/15,945 sq mi

Political System Liberal democracy

Flag The flag may have been based on that of Schwyz, one of the original cantons of the Confederation. While the national flag is square, a rectangular flag is used on Swiss lakes and rivers.

I-SPY points: 5

Date: _____

I-SPY points: 5

Date: _____

TAIWAN
formerly Formosa (until 1949)

Capital Taipei

Language Chinese (dialects include Mandarin (official), Min, and Hakka)

Currency New Taiwan dollar

Population 23,188,000

Area 36,179 sq km/13,968 sq mi

Political System Emergent democracy

Flag Known as 'white sun in blue sky', the flag of Chinese revolutionary leader Sun Zhong Shan appears in the canton. The rays of the sun represent 12 traditional Chinese hours (each equalling two hours) symbolizing progress. Red is a traditional Chinese colour.

TANZANIA
formerly Tanganyika (until 1964)

Capital Dodoma (official), Dar es Salaam (administrative)

Language Kiswahili, English (both official), Arabic (in Zanzibar), many local languages

Currency Tanzanian shilling

Population 43,739,000

Area 945,000 sq km/ 364,864 sq mi

Political System Emergent democracy

Flag Green stands for the forests and agriculture. Gold symbolizes the country's mineral wealth. Blue represents the sea.

I-SPY points: 15

<u>Date:</u> _____

I-SPY points: 20

<u>Date:</u> _____

THAILAND

formerly Siam (until 1939 and 1945–49)

Capital Bangkok (and chief port)

Language Thai, Chinese (both official), English, Lao, Malay, Khmer

Currency Baht

Population 67,764,000

Area 513,115 sq km/ 198,113 sq mi

Political System Emergent democracy

Flag The central band was originally red. It was changed to blue to express solidarity with the Allies during World War I.

TUNISIA

Capital Tunis (and chief port)

Language Arabic (official), French

Currency Tunisian dinar

Population 10,272,000

Area 164,150 sq km/ 63,378 sq mi

Political System Nationalistic socialist

Flag The flag was introduced by Hassan II, the Bey of Tunisia. Red is an Islamic colour.

I-SPY points: 20

Date: _____

I-SPY points: 15

Date: _____

TURKEY

Capital Ankara (administrative), Istanbul (commercial)

Language Turkish (official), Kurdish, Arabic

Currency New Turkish lira

Population 74,816,700

Area 779,500 sq km/ 300,964 sq mi

Political System Liberal democracy

Flag The star, which was added to the flag in 1793, initially had more than five points. The star may represent the Morning Star mentioned in the Koran.

UGANDA

Capital Kampala

Language English (official), Kiswahili, other Bantu and Nilotic languages

Currency Ugandan new shilling

Population 32,710,000

Area 236,600 sq km/ 91,351 sq mi

Political System Authoritarian nationalist

Flag Red symbolizes the brotherhood of man. Black represents the African people. Yellow stands for sunshine.

I-SPY points: 10

Date: _____

I-SPY points: 20

Date: _____

58

UKRAINE

Capital Kiev

Language Ukrainian (a Slavonic language; official), Russian (also official in Crimea), other regional languages

Currency Hryvna

Population 45,708,000

Area 603,700 sq km/ 233,088 sq mi

Political System Emergent democracy

Flag The national colours are taken from the Rusyn arms of 1848.

UNITED ARAB EMIRATES

formerly Trucial States (until 1968), Federation of Arab Emirates (with Bahrain and Qatar) (1968–71)

Capital Abu Dhabi

Language Arabic (official), Farsi, Hindi, Urdu, English

Currency UAE dirham

Population 4,599,000

Area 83,657 sq km/ 32,299 sq mi

Political System Absolutist

Flag Green is a symbol of fertility. White represents neutrality. Black reflects the Emirates' oil wealth. Red recalls the former flags of the Kharijite Muslims.

I-SPY points: 15

Date:

I-SPY points: 15

Date:

UNITED KINGDOM

Capital London

Language English (official), Welsh (also official in Wales), Gaelic

Currency Pound sterling

Population 61,565,000

Area 244,100 sq km/ 94,247 sq mi

Political System Liberal democracy

Flag The white saltire comes from the flag of Scotland. The St Patrick's Cross was, in fact, taken from the arms of the powerful Geraldine family. The red cross of St George is taken from the flag of England.

UNITED STATES OF AMERICA

Capital Washington, DC

Language English, Spanish

Currency US dollar

Population 314,659,000

Area 9,826,632 sq km/ 3,794,084 sq mi

Political System Liberal democracy

Flag Red stands for hardiness and valour. White signifies purity and innocence. Blue represents vigilance, perseverance, and justice. The latest star, representing Hawaii, was added in 1960. The 50 stars represent the 50 states making up the USA.

I-SPY points: 5

Date: _____

I-SPY points: 5

Date: _____

URUGUAY

Capital Montevideo

Language Spanish (official),
Brazilero (a mixture of Spanish
and Portuguese)

Currency Uruguayan peso

Population 3,361,000

Area 176,200 sq km/
68,030 sq mi

Political System Liberal
democracy

Flag The flag is modelled on the
Stars and Stripes of the United
States' flag. The stripes represent
the nine provinces at the time
of liberation. Blue and white are
the colours of Argentina and
also of national hero, José
Gervasio Artigas.

I-SPY points: 10

Date: _____

VENEZUELA

Capital Caracas

Language Spanish (official),
Indian languages (2%)

Currency Bolivar

Population 28,583,000

Area 912,100 sq km/
352,161 sq mi

Political System Liberal
democracy

Flag Yellow symbolizes the
golden land of South America.
Red stands for courage and the
blood of the freedom fighters.
Blue represents the ocean
separating South America
from Spain.

I-SPY points: 15

Date: _____

VIETNAM

formerly part of French Indo-China (1884–1945), Democratic Republic of Vietnam (in north) (1945–75), Republic of Vietnam (in south) (1949–75)

Capital Hanoi

Language Vietnamese (official), French, English, Khmer, Chinese, local languages

Currency Dong

Population 88,069,000

Area 329,600 sq km/ 127,258 sq mi

Political System Communist

Flag The five points of the star represent the unity of farmers, workers, intellectuals, soldiers, and youth in establishing socialism. Red stands for revolution and bloodshed.

ZIMBABWE

formerly Southern Rhodesia (until 1980)

Capital Harare

Language English, Shona, Ndebele (all official)

Currency Zimbabwe dollar

Population 12,523,000

Area 390,300 sq km/ 150,694 sq mi

Political System Nationalistic socialist

Flag Yellow stands for mineral wealth. Green represents the country's vegetation and natural resources. Red recalls the blood spilt during the liberation struggle.

I-SPY points: 20

Date: _____

I-SPY points: 20

Date: _____

Index

First published by Michelin Maps and Guides 2009
© Michelin, Propriétaires-Editeurs 2009.
Michelin and the Michelin Man are registered Trademarks of Michelin.
Created and produced by Horizons Publishing Limited.
All rights reserved. No part of this publication may be reproduced, copied or transmitted in any form without the prior consent of the publisher. Print services by FingerPrint International Book production - fingerprint@pandora.be
The publisher gratefully acknowledges the contribution of the I-Spy team: Camilla Lovell and Ruth Neilson in the production of this title.
Original flag data and illustrations copyright RM, 2009.
All rights reserved.
Helicon Publishing is a division of RM.

HOW TO GET YOUR I-SPY CERTIFICATE AND BADGE

Every time you score 1000 points or more in an I-Spy book, you can apply for a certificate

Here's what to do, step by step:

Certificate

- Ask an adult to check your score
- Ask his or her permission to apply for a certificate
- Apply online to www.ispymichelin.com
- Enter your name and address and the completed title
- We will send you back via e mail your certificate for the title

Badge

- Each I-Spy title has a cut out (page corner) token at the back of the book
- Collect five tokens from different I-Spy titles
- Put Second Class Stamps on two strong envelopes
- Write your own address on one envelope and put a £1 coin inside it (for protection). Fold, but do not seal the envelope, and place it inside the second envelope
- Write the following address on the second envelope, seal it carefully and post to:

I-Spy Books
Michelin Maps and Guides
Hannay House
39 Clarendon Road
Watford
WD17 1JA